# _The_ **Oldie**
# **More Cartoons**

# More Cartoons

*Chosen by*

*Richard Ingrams*

Oldie Publications Ltd
London

This compilation first published by
Oldie Publications Ltd

Copyright © 1996 Oldie Publications Ltd

The publishers would like to thank the respective copyright owners
for permission to include illustrations in this volume

A CIP catalogue record for this book is available from
The British Library

ISBN 1 901170 01 2

Covers printed by Amica Fine Print Ltd
Text printed and bound by Woolnough Bookbinding Ltd
Design and production by Richard Adams Associates
Cover illustration by Michael Forman

# Introduction

Since founding the *Oldie* in 1992, I now find that the best part of my office routine is spent sifting through the vast pile of cartoons that accumulates every day on my desk.

I do not complain about this. In fact the more that come in, the more I admire the invention and the tenacity of the artists especially when something like 98% of the cartoons are returned with the bleak message – 'Sorry not this time'.

Despite my choosiness and the scarcely generous remuneration on offer, I think I can justifiably claim that the *Oldie* now has the best, most varied selection of cartoons of any magazine in the country (and probably the world).

My thanks, again, to the talented team of men and women who have made my proud boast a reality.

Richard Ingrams
July 1996

'Winning the lottery hasn't changed us –
we're still here!'

*'Have you noticed a significant ageing of the local population?'*

'We got us a nice quiet little town here, mister, and I aim to keep it that way!'

'Go! And never darken my doorstep again!'

'Excuse me sir. This is a gentlemen's evening'

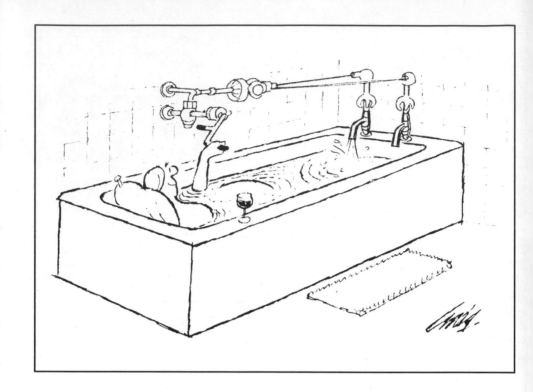

'We met on 'Blind Date'!'

'Yeah...I dropped out of obedience school too'

'Heinz or Campbells?'

'Rise and Shine!'          'No thanks, I don't need a pee'

'In compliance with Rule 1(a) of the Union of Jazz Drummers we now
interrupt the music for a ten minute drum solo'

'Moses – how many times must I tell you? Stop playing with your soup!'

'He misses the Cones Hotline more than he'll admit'

*'Just how many lawn-sprinkling violations does he have?'*

*'The gods are mildly irritated tonight'*

*'We must have lunch some time'*

'I can't seem to contact the deceased —
only his answering machine'

'It's another bloody fatwah!'

'Well I feel just the same, I'd pack the job in too if it wasn't for the free uniform...'

'Now here come the drinks again...'

*'How do you like your beans?'*

GARDEN PARTY
SATURDAY 2.30
OPENED BY
SIR MORTIMER CROW M.P
STAR OF:
"MINISTER IN WHITEHALL NUDE SEX TRIANGLE"

*Abbot and Castella*

'I see you've been destitute in five major cities'

'We thank you, Lord, for that which we are about to receive, excepting, perhaps, the trace amounts of naturally ocurring carcinogens, that, in your mysterious way, you've included in the turkey and bread stuffing.'

'What, no film crew?'

'We've been nominated for
the Turner Prize'

'Manager? This weekend special of yours with four-poster bedroom...'

'I've had a poke round your subconscious. We're talking about seven grand'

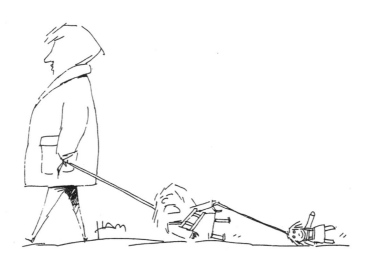

*'And don't forget your optician's appointment'*

*'Why don't you look like the doctors in the TV serials?'*

'Look on the bright side, missus — at least he has a bed!'

'Do you mind – some of us
work nights'

'The railway gave it to me when I retired'

'Operator – I'd like to make a parson to parson call'

'I wish you'd stop putting me on a pedestal, darling'

*'I'd say he's critical but stable'*

*'We guarantee the quality of our meat by documenting its history from pasture to plate'*

'What year is the spring water?'

Nick Downes

*'Oh my God – and she belongs to Friends of the Earth!'*

'I didn't think our divorce would be so amicable that you'd still be here'

'I can't do it – I've got executioner's block'

'Maurice Bulstrode, VAT inspector,
The Spanish Inquisition'

*'It's neighbourhood watch — Jehovah's witnesses approaching'*

*'I'm new here — where's the recording studio?'*

*'I'm sorry, ma'am, but until he actually does something, there's nothing we can do'*

'I'll have the strawberries, with a double helping of fat-cat cream'

'It's a take-over bid'

THINKTANK

'It's a new pools coupon: you've got
to select the eight teams that sack their
managers this week'

'My wife doesn't understand
my computer...'

'He's on holiday'

'You're beautiful when you're counselling, Miss Bedwelty'

'I can't stand this foreign muck – gimme a pizza or a curry any day'

'How about Best of Three?'

*'So it wasn't a mis-spelling, then'*

*'Miss Thompson — take a suicide note'*

'These "Three Tenors" – are they going to be the new Beatles?'

'What say you to the idea of running a lottery Merlin?'

'I've seen it all – a surrealist pavement artist'

'I see another Sunday paper has been re-launched'

'Any plans for the next millennium?'

'I see that more and more people are working out of the home'

'That trial and verdict caused you grievous stress. We're going for compensation'

'Maureen and I are going through a bit of a rough patch!'

'He says he's "Dad" – shall I ask
for identification?'

'Looks like another brutal murder, officer'

'Well, you know best, Grandma. I hope you'll be very happy together'

'So I said to him, I said pink? Pink with those curtains? You must be mad'

*'…and ease off on the coffee mornings'*

*'Yes! But is it art?'*

*'Girls we've struck lucky – it's Tom, Dick and Harry'*

*'I can feel one of my bloody awful turns coming on!'*

'Watch out for the queue-jumper,
pass it on!'

'Good evening, sir. I represent
Watchdog Security. Do you realize
how vulnerable you are?'

'Can I borrow the mobile phone
tonight Dad?'

'Can you put me on hold again? That's my favourite tune'

'This is all there is, minus a small service charge'

*'You got to hand it to him, doing all his own stunts at his age'*

'Mr Poskett, your wife has already brought the charge of mental cruelty to my attention, and quite frankly, you're not helping matters...'

'Charlie believed in living in the fast lane'

'Ssh!'

'We've all had to go metric, it's a 45.4 litre'

Reading

Rigby.

'I've just been through a rather messy divorce'

'How many ounces in a Kilometre?'

GED

'Someone ate the spud you liked.
Try this one, sir...'

'Frankly I think it's a monstrous
invasion of my privacy'

*'Do we have to go through this every time you use the underground Norman?'*

*'Bob's taken the dog for a walk'*

'Make the most of it while you can!'

'They suspect arson'

'You spoil that dog'

'When you pass the newsagent, would you cancel the "Daily Mail" and "Hello"?'

'Big date tonight, Dad...can I borrow your teeth?'

'Would you care to step outside and repeat that remark?'

'I'm sick of these power failures!'

*'Whilst you were out, the government revived our flagging fortunes'*

*'Miss Honeyball, I smell money. Check it out, will you?'*

*'You're rather over-qualified for this job'*

'I find there's far too much violence in cave paintings these days'

# Superdupermar

'That'll be £289.95 and do you require counselling?'

'How mushy do you like your peas?'

'George! You know shell-fish doesn't agree with you!'

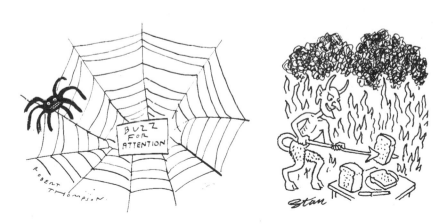

'…and this is Sylvia and me, going through a bad patch…'

'There's been one or two nibbles, but no definite offers'

'Your X-ray shows a thin man struggling to get out'

*'Isn't it wonderful how Robert has continued to evolve?'*

*'Yes, we are Mr and Mrs Smith,
but we want to book in as Mr Pearson and
Miss Jones, just to make it more exciting'*

*'That's a company tea-mug,
Tompkins. I want it back'*

*'Lottery'*

*'Looks like the blighter's given us the slip again'*

*'You just can't help feeling he's setting himself up for one more disappointment'*

*'I didn't have the heart to sack him'*

'Mum, Dad, they followed me home..!
Can we keep them?!!'

'Susan! The milk is boiling over!'

'Harry! – there's a spider in the bath'

'Sssssh, you'll wake the baby!'

*'Are things really that bad, or are we just not allowed to smoke in here?'*

'Could I see the milk list?'

'Are we allowed a feelgood factor'

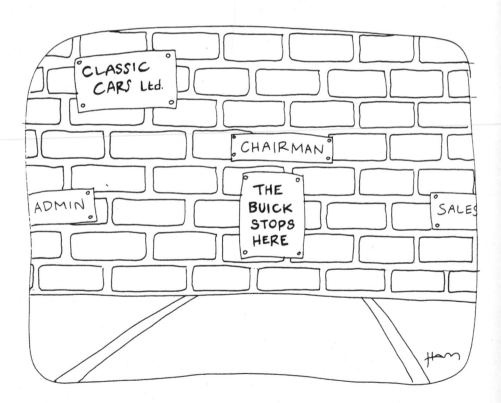

'How can we possibly have an intelligent discussion if you keep butting in...?'

'Oh dear, lost are you? Well what
does your mum look like?'

'Who's the one in drag?'

*'Uncles Ted's almost become part of the furniture in this house now'*

'This is Bill. He's sharing my life in the parish'

cooper

*'Could you suggest something that would re-invigorate our waning relationship?'*

*'When ads like this drive you to drink, try one of these...'*

'It says his name is "Tramp".'

*'It's the government's new Care-in-the-Community initiative'*

'He's definitely teething'

'...Dear Sir,...'

'How would you feel about being thrown in at the deep end'

'Am I free for a nervous breakdown on Tuesday?'

'I'm just frightened I'm going to be left
on the Continental Shelf'

'Just looking...'

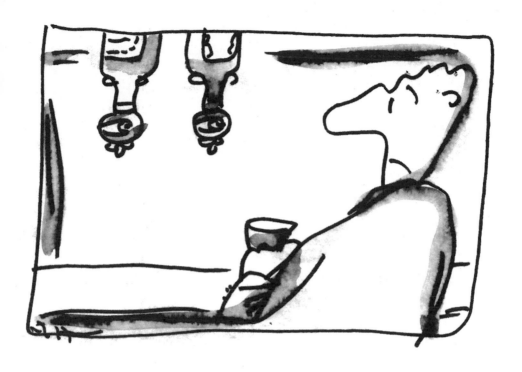

'No pudding for him – he didn't eat his greens!'

'Bad news I'm afraid, Sergeant. You're going to be privatised'

'I told you we were over-dressed'

K. Lamb

'I understand you've taken a vow of silence...'

'We're hoping to be re-cycled'

'Are the bees free range?'

'He wants to see his money before he goes...'

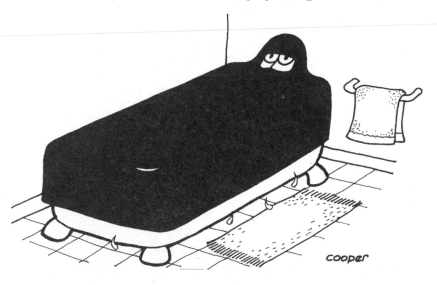

cooper

*'I told you not to call when there's no-one near me!'*

*'Remind me to tell Parsons to ring these Camelot people, my dear, we appear to have won the jackpot!'*

'Hey, its not that bad!'

'Is the defendant aware of the seriousness of the charge?'

'You can have one of my marbles Grandad, Mummy says you've lost yours'

BATH
SUPPLIED BY
YORKSHIRE
WATER

'…Better sit down, son – I've got a bit of a shock for you'

'I know we promised not to make any more promises that we couldn't keep but we didn't mean it'

*'Could you make it a little longer?'*

*'This calls for a celebration — let's open a can of worms!'*

*'Luckily, I'm wearing
my family planning
hat today'*

*'I can't hold on much longer and quite frankly
you're not helping!'*

'Surely someone *knows how to drive*…?

'Friends, Romans, genetically-engineered mice…'

'I've been downsized'

'I swear by almighty Reebok...'

ROOM FOR
6 SEATED
1 LYING DOWN

'George was DNA Tested last week but they couldn't find any'

'Soup of the day's crap by the way'

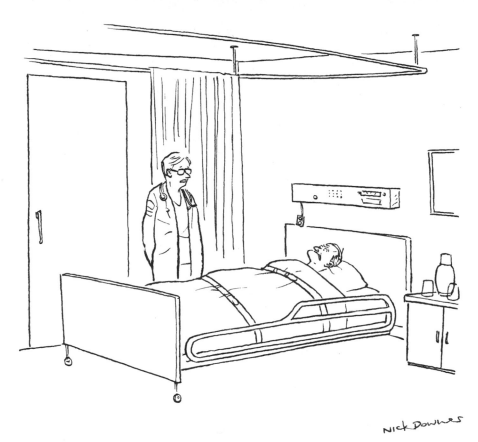

'The restraints are for your own protection Mr Norris. We're concerned that if you ring the nurses desk once more, they'll strangle you'

'Hello, we're Jehovah's Widnes'

'I'm afraid your tie is not quite worn enough...'

*'I'm cancelling my cosmetic surgery appointment with him. Just look at the way he handles a knife!'*

*'Remember, you're accused of witchcraft so try not to cackle... and lose the hat!'*

*'I'd say it was more a cry for help than a serious suicide attempt'*

*'Got anything in gangland?'*